1—1

Glenn McCracken
New Castle Area Schools
New Castle, Pennsylvania

Charles C. Walcutt
Queens College
Flushing, New York

BASIC READING

J. B. LIPPINCOTT COMPANY
Philadelphia New York

CONTENTS

sh

she ship shin shaft shed shot
shun shut short sheep sheet
shine shape shade shock shall
share shirt shell shone rash splash
rush sash dash dish gash cash hash
hush lash plush flash flush trash
fish wish

wash push

A Fish Tale

Sam and Ben went up Pine Creek to fish. Sam had an old boat and oars. Ben had two fish poles. He gave one to Sam.

"Shall we fish from the shore?" asked Ben. "Or shall we wade in the water?"

"Let us fish from the shore," said Sam. "We will scare the fish if we wade in the water."

two one

"I got one!" said Ben. "It is a big fish."

"I have one, too!" said Sam. "It is a bass."

Sam and Ben landed five more fish.

"I will make a fire," Sam told Ben. "We will bake two fish for us to eat."

Sam and Ben had a fine meal of fish.

"Now we must start home," said Sam.

too

"The boat is not here," said Ben. "It is not on the shore."

"I see the boat," Sam told Ben. "It is in the stream. We will wade to the boat and take the fish home in it."

Ben had the fish in a can. He fell on a rock. Splash! Splash! went the fish as all five swam down the creek.

"We have lost all five fish," said Sam, "and we have got wet. But we had fun, and we had fish to eat."

ch

chat chap Chet chin chip chill
chop chow chum cheek cheer chess
cheat chirp chase check cheese
charm chose chalk chick chest each
punch pinch bench bunch lunch
hunch rich such much teach reach
peach beach porch scorch torch

tch

pitch patch ditch Dutch catch
match hatch hitch batch watch
snatch latch pitcher fetch

Chin Chin

Chin Chin sits on a short old
bench
And eats from a dish of cheese.
He eats so much and gets so full
He cannot sit at ease.

"I must not fall from the bench,"
cries Chin,
"Or the cat will catch me, I fear,
And eat me for lunch as I ate the
cheese.
He is such a bad cat, I hear."

But Chin Chin goes to sleep
at last,
And he falls from the bench on
his chest.
And the cat eats Chin Chin in two
big bites,
And sits down on the porch to rest.

Chin was a pig to eat so much
And fall asleep as he did.
It made him too full to be awake,
So off the bench he slid.

th

the then this that these those thus
them than thin thick thank think
thump throat thrush three thrift
throb with oath teeth bath
thirst third girth mirth
thorn forth north

other brother mother
father together

there they

Red Hen

Red Hen lived in an old barn. She had ten chicks. The chicks liked to run in the grass. If her chicks ran too far, Red Hen called them back.

"This hen is mine," Kate told Bob. "These chicks are mine, too. I feed them mash. Red Hen eats corn and oats."

Once Red Hen lost one of her chicks. Its name was Peep Peep.

"We must find it," said Kate.

Bob and Kate went to find Peep Peep.

"Here it is," said Bob. "I see Peep Peep in this tall grass. I will get the chick for Red Hen."

As Bob went to pick up Peep Peep, he saw a big hawk. Hawks like to eat chicks. Hawks have sharp claws.

Bob got Peep Peep just in time. Peep Peep was glad to get back home.

Flop Ears

Flop Ears was an old mule. He had big ears and a thick skin. Once Tom drove him to town. The mule came to a hole in the road. He sat down. Mules will not go past a hole in the road if the hole is deep.

mule

Thump! Thump! Thump! Tom hit Flop Ears on the back with his stick. But Flop Ears just sat in the dust. He had thick skin.

"I cannot take Flop Ears to town with me," said Tom. "He will not go past such a deep hole. I think we must go back home."

Just then a man came down the road. He sat down to chat with Tom. Flop Ears still sat in the dust.

"I can make the mule go past the hole," said the man.

"No, you cannot!" said Tom. "If you can make Flop Ears go past the hole, I will give him to you."

"Fine, fine," said the man. "First, I will fill the hole. Then I will drive Flop Ears past it."

you

The man put dirt in the hole and drove the mule past it. Tom gave the mule to the man and went home.

His wife told him he must get Flop Ears back. “The man did not drive the mule past a hole,” she said. “The hole is full of dirt now. It is not a hole at all.”

wh

when wheat wheel whip while which
white whirl whether whisper
what where
who

Tom Finds Flop Ears

Tom went to the town to get his mule. He had a whip.

"I will make Flop Ears come home with me if I can find him," said Tom.

When Tom got to the town, he saw nine mules.

"Where is Flop Ears? Which mule is mine?" asked Tom. "I can see nine mules. One is white. He is not my mule. All of the mules but the white one are brown like Flop Ears. What shall I do?"

"Here, Flop Ears! Here, Flop Ears!" said Tom.

When Flop Ears saw Tom, he came at once. Tom got on his mule and rode to the gate.

The man who had the mule came to speak to him. "What is this?" he said. "You cannot take this mule. He is mine."

"I can take him! I can take him!" said Tom. "When you drove him past the hole, it was not a hole at all. So, the mule is mine."

Tom rode Flop Ears home and fed him wheat and oats. Then Tom went to tell his wife that Flop Ears was safe in the barn.

qu

queen quilt quit quick quail quack quill

A quaint snail
Has left his trail,
So fragile,
So frail
On a thorn.

In a quiet refrain,
A gentle rain
Washed away
His faint trail
In the morn.

—Adele H. Seronde

X

tax fox box ox ax six wax Max sox
fix mix

A vixen is a fox.
A vixen is a fox.
Fox-in-den
Fox-in-den
A vixen is a fox.

—Adele H. Seronde

y

yes yell yelp yet you yard year yarn

I am an elf.
Yes, I am an elf.
An elf not as big
as a man—

Not as big as a bat
In a box, I will sit
On the end of a pin,
if I can!

—Adele H. Seronde

Z

zip zest zero zone zebra fizz buzz fuzz

Buzz, buzz
I sip honey
From the lip
Of a red
Poppy.

—Adele H. Seronde

I Can Be Anyone

I can
  Jump as a robin
I can
  Hum as a bee
I can
  Hop on a twig
As a chick-a-dee-dee!

I can
  Run as a red fox
I can buzz as a fly—
I can be
  Anyone!
But no one
  Can be I!

—Adele H. Seronde

At the Park

Don Jones asked his father to take him to the park. His father said, "Yes, I will take you, but it is time to eat lunch. I will take you some other time, Don."

The next time Don asked his father, it was not lunch time yet. So off went Don and Father to the park to see the wild birds and animals.

At the park, the zebra ran back and forth on the grass in a big yard. He lived and grazed there.

The yak and the musk ox just watched Don and his father.

The six ducks in the pond swam with quick strokes to the shore. "Quack, quack," the ducks said.

On the shore, a line of quail ran to the tall grass.

Don gazed for a while. Then he said, "Are the wild animals cared for here in the park?"

"Yes," said his father. "But when the wild animals were free, they had to hunt for meat to eat. The animals had to run and hide from each other and from men with guns. Ducks hid from foxes and hawks and men with guns. The zebra had to run from the lion. The hare ran from the fox."

“Do some wild animals not have to run at all?” asked Don.

“Well,” said his father, “the lion and his mate are called the king and queen of the forest. But the tiger is just as big and brave.”

“And,” he went on, “the lion and the tiger are big. They need much to eat. They have to hunt all the time. They have to hunt to catch meat to fill them up.”

"It must be better for them to be here in the park. There is much for them to eat here," said Don.

"Yes," said his father. "Yet some think that wild animals like best to live free in the forest. Do you think so, Don?"

"No, I don't think so," said Don. "The wild animals are not like men. I think they like to be cared for here in the park."

ng

sing sang sung song ring rang rung
ding dong tong thing ping pong
pang hang hung fang wing long lung
bang king gong swing fling bring
spring sprang sprung strong string
strung

A Song of Spring

Spring is a time when all is fresh
And birds sing songs in the trees.
Spring is a time when roses bud
And bring sweet smells in the breeze.

Spring is a time when the leaves are
green
And the grass gets long and thick.
It is just the time to string up a kite
And go to fish in the creek.

Spring is a time when cow bells ring,
Ding, dong! Ding, dong! Ding, dong!
And tree frogs sing so strong and clear
And the bees hum a buzzing song.

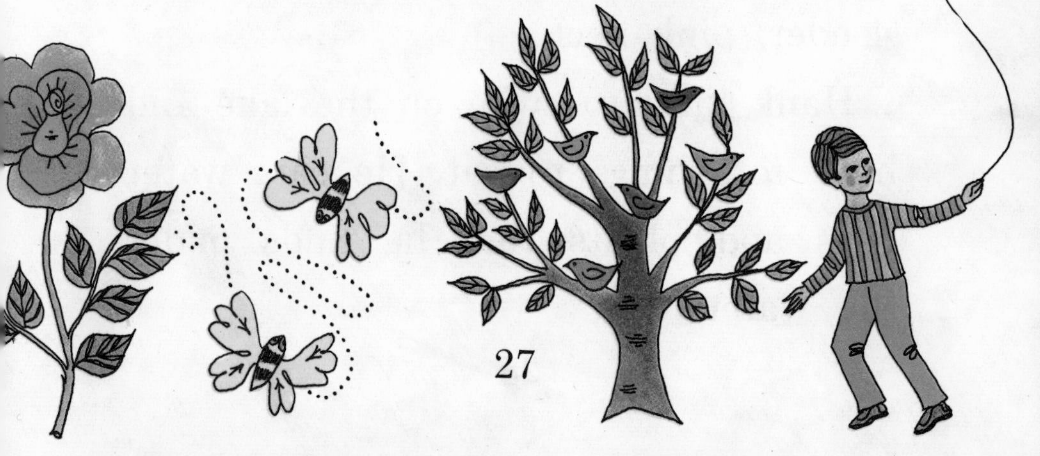

The Pink Swan

Have you ever seen a pink swan? Most swans are white, but this one is more pink than white. His name is Hank. He has pink wings and a long, slender, pink neck.

Hank likes to swim on the lake and hunt for things to eat. He eats water bugs and plants that he finds under the water.

Hank can catch a water bug as quick as a wink. When he wants a plant to eat, he ducks his long neck into the water. Then he pulls up the plant with his bill.

Once a mink came to the lake. He came to find a duck to eat.

Minks like to scare swans if they see them first. But swans are too big for minks to eat.

This mink came to the bank of the lake where Hank hunted for things to eat. The mink dug a hole in the weeds and hid in it.

When Hank came to hunt for bugs, the mink sprang into the lake to scare him.

But Hank saw the mink first. He made his legs and wings go fast.

This mink did not scare Hank. Hank was a smart swan.

Bells

Cling, clang!
The bells rang
Cling, clong!
A wild song!
A wild song
Bells have sung—
Cling, clong!
Bells have rung!

—Adele H. Seronde

Do you see the parts?

into	milkman	bedtime	cupcake
streetcar	pancake	lipstick	shotgun
sunshine	oatmeal	himself	herself
sunspot	dishpan	rainstorm	inside
railroad	roadside	dustpan	hailstorm
wheatcake	flapjack	topcoat	baseball
milkmaid	topmost	raincoat	beside

overcoat	pineapple	peppermint
butterfly	grandmother	grandfather
suppertime	basketball	supermarket

ing

singing	dressing	jumping	bringing
helping	selling	pitching	standing
sending	thinking	catching	checking
sticking	packing	licking	locking
smacking	tracking	asking	thumping
patching	matching	hatching	marching
listing	longing	stalling	planting
quilting	quacking	thanking	whirling
ringing	hanging	sinking	swinging
winking	chirping	camping	willing

feeding seeding meeting needing
keeping peeking peeling feeling peeping
reading eating leaning seating leaping
cheating beating feasting dreaming
reaching teaching fearing leading
beaming steaming sealing floating
boating roaring groaning roaming
soaking foaming soaping soaring
roasting toasting coasting boasting

Catching Fish

A big black bear is fishing in the lake. He is standing near the shore where the lake is not deep. The bear is smacking his lips. He is thinking how the fish will taste when he eats them.

The bear is catching more fish than he can eat. When he is full of fish, he will leave the rest on the shore. A fox or a mink will come and eat them.

ing

digging	hopping	rubbing	running
spinning	sitting	letting	skipping
patting	tapping	cutting	planning
sunning	chopping	stopping	getting
slapping	shutting	robbing	winning
napping	popping	pinning	hitting
humming	dipping	mapping	mopping
nodding	ripping	rotting	sagging
setting	tipping	grinning	gripping
petting	fanning	fitting	hugging
flapping	flopping		

The Hare and the Fox

A small, brown hare was sitting near a creek sunning himself, when he saw a fox. The fox was getting a drink in the small stream.

The hare ran from his nest, but the fox saw him hopping in the grass. Quick as a wink, the fox was running to catch the hare.

The brown hare ran into a hole in an old log. The hole was too small for a fox.

As the hare ran from the hole, he saw the fox digging to get into it.

When the fox got inside the old log, he did not find a hare. All he saw was a hole as long as the log.

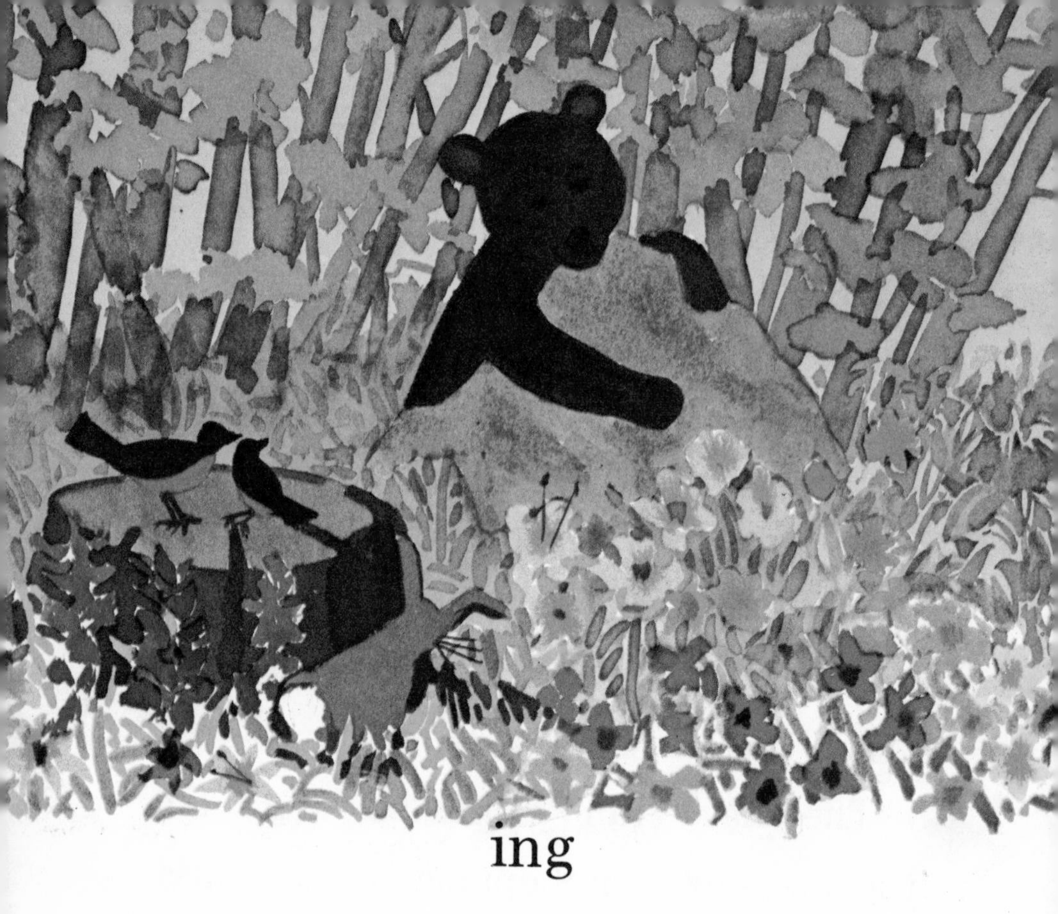

ing

chasing riding smoking hoping poking
snoring voting diving waving paving
saving dining hiding baking taking
tasting taming staring waking shining
biting smiling naming making gazing
raking joking dozing liking pasting
shaking quaking spading gliding
blazing trading blaming flaming
stoning sloping teasing

Hiking

Jack went hiking on the bank of a lake. It was a fine time to be hiking. The sun was blazing and the robins sang in the trees.

Jack had fun on his hike. He spent most of the time chasing rabbits and dozing in the shade.

All at once Jack saw a bear hiding near a rock. Then the bear was poking his nose into a hole in a tree. A swarm of bees came from the hole. The bees stung the bear. Then Jack saw the bees chasing the bear. As the bear ran, he was biting at the bees. Jack saw the bear diving into the water.

"I think I will go home," said Jack to himself. "I do not want the bear or the bees to chase me."

A Ride on a Sled

Bill and Joan went coasting on a big hill. At the top of the hill Bill said, "I will sit in front and steer the sled, Joan. You sit in the back so that you can hold on to me."

Down the hill went the sled with Bill and Joan hanging on to it. It

went so fast that Joan had a feeling that she was floating. She was leaning on Bill and calling to him to stop the sled.

The sled went too fast for Bill to stop it. So he and Joan just held on.

As the sled came to a steep part of the hill, it struck a bump in the path. Then it went leaping into the snow.

snow

Joan and Bill fell from the sled into a big pile of snow.

"Where are you, Joan?" said Bill. "I cannot see you."

"I am here," said Joan, peeking from the pile of snow. "I am stuck in the deep snow, and I am soaking wet."

ed

toast	last	plant	coast
toasted	lasted	planted	coasted
fold	load	rest	boast
folded	loaded	rested	boasted
need	start	list	land
needed	started	listed	landed
add	print	call	kill
added	printed	called	killed
form	harm	dream	burn
formed	harmed	dreamed	burned

charm peel jump mark
charmed peeled jumped marked

march wish thank splash
marched wished thanked splashed

hitch pitch chirp pinch
hitched pitched chirped pinched

puff sniff stuff fuss
puffed sniffed stuffed fussed

ed

pot	rot	dot	spot
potted	rotted	dotted	spotted
plot	plan	pin	flop
plotted	planned	pinned	flopped
stop	skip	trip	flip
stopped	skipped	tripped	flipped
tip	rip	sip	dip
tipped	ripped	sipped	dipped

trade	taste	hate	date	fade
traded	tasted	hated	dated	faded

state	note	shade	waste
stated	noted	shaded	wasted

name	flame	blame	tame	tape
named	flamed	blamed	tamed	taped

pare	snore	smile	wave	save
pared	snored	smiled	waved	saved

blaze	gaze	shine	shame	shape
blazed	gazed	shined	shamed	shaped

share	tease	care	dare	chase
shared	teased	cared	dared	chased

rope	spare	hope	snare	like
roped	spared	hoped	snared	liked

smoke	poke	bake	joke
smoked	poked	baked	joked

A Fire

Jim lived on a farm. He had horses and cows in a big barn on his farm.

Once Jim saw a fire burning near his barn. He did not want his horses and cows to be burned. Jim ran to see what was burning. When he reached the fire, he saw that it was burning dried grass and weeds.

First, he ran into the barn to save his horses and cows. He led them to a safer part of the farm.

burn

"I must stop this fire," said Jim, "or the barn will be burned."

Jim needed help to stop the fire. It was too big for one man to stop. "Help! Help!" yelled Jim.

A man named Walt lived on the next farm. Walt jumped on his truck and drove to the farm to help Jim. Walt had a hose, a pump, and a big tank of water.

Walt watched for small flames. When he saw one, he squirted water on it with the hose.

The fire blazed and hissed in one patch. Then it flamed up in other spots where the dried grass was thick.

At last, the two men stopped the fire.

It had burned quite near the barn and scorched it. But the barn did not burn, and the horses and cows were saved.

"What started the fire?" asked Walt. "Did you strike a match in the weeds?"

"No," said Jim. "I did not start it. But I must not leave dried grass and weeds so close to the barn. Next time, I will rake them into piles and burn them far from the barn."

Jim thanked Walt for helping him. Then he started to rake up all the dried grass and weeds that had not burned.

"I must keep the barn safe," he said. "It is full of horses and cows and oats and wheat."

er

her jerk herd term fern clerk

faster longer shorter floater helper
planter sender loader farmer printer
killer camper jumper pitcher starter
catcher marker thicker sicker picker
pincher richer steeper reader feeler
eater neater beater leader leaner
quicker buzzer older hunter singer
stronger blacker colder kinder

rider riper miner finer taster timer
hater chaser maker riser smoker
trader baker driver diner poker

winter summer better under letter
corner dinner never sister supper ever
mister

shopper thinner spinner redder
clapper chopper slipper flatter flipper
hotter cutter fitter swimmer upper
robber winner digger planner rubber
runner sitter drummer dipper bigger

ar

dollar poplar beggar grammar forward
backward

ir

sir fir stir dirt first girl birth third
thirst chirp

or

word work worth world worse doctor
flavor tailor sailor armor actor harbor

ur

fur burn turn hurt curb purr curl

Can You Tell?

When do the robins first chirp
and sing,
Winter, summer, fall, or spring?

When does an oak leaf turn to
red,
And the first frost fall on
the flower bed?

When is it hotter than spring
or fall—
When the sun shines longer and
the grass gets tall?

When can the skaters glide
fast on the lakes,
And hunters track deer in the
soft snowflakes?

A Thinking Beggar

Once a beggar had tramped five miles in the hot sun. He was quite tired and wanted to rest. As he came to a crossroads, he saw a poplar tree. On one side of the tree he saw a board. "Take This Road To Franklin" was printed on the board.

"I will rest under the tree," said the beggar. "I can lean on that board while I sleep."

As the beggar slept, a doctor rode up to him.

"Wake up, beggar!" said the doctor. "I am lost. Can you tell me which road to take to Franklin?"

"It is too hot to think," said the beggar. "Thinking is work in such heat."

"Here is a dollar," said the doctor. "Now, will you think?"

"Indeed, I will, sir!" said the beggar. "Take that road to Franklin."

Then a tailor stopped to ask the beggar which road to take to Franklin.

"It is worth a dollar," said the beggar, "for me to start thinking."

The tailor gave him a dollar. "Turn to the left," the beggar said.

The beggar went back to sleep. Before long a sailor was shaking him. "Which is the road to Franklin?" he asked. The beggar got another dollar, and the sailor went down the road.

"A doctor gets paid when he doctors," said the beggar to himself. "A tailor gets paid when he tailors, and a sailor gets paid when he sails. But this time a beggar got paid, and all he did was think!"

Dark Star

A man named Ted had a fine horse farm. In the wintertime he kept his horses in a red barn. The barn was warm and clean.

One of the horses was called Dark Star. He was a white horse with a black star on his forehead. Dark Star was born at the horse farm. He liked his big, clean stall and the warm coat he wore in winter.

When Ted wanted to go horseback riding, he chose Dark Star. This horse

forehead

was a fast runner. Whenever all of the horses ran, Dark Star came in first.

Once a man came in a car to see Ted. Ted spoke with him on the front porch. The man wanted to trade his car to Ted for Dark Star.

Ted liked Dark Star and did not want to trade him. But he liked the car, too. "I have more horses," said Ted, "and I do need a car. I will trade Dark Star to you for this car."

Ted felt sad as he saw the man riding Dark Star to the barnyard gate. "Will Dark Star miss his old home?"

Ted asked himself. "And will I miss the best riding horse I ever had?"

Ted rode all over the farm in his car. It was not as much fun as riding Dark Star. "A horse is better to ride on a farm," he said. "A car cannot go over big bumps of dirt and logs. And a car is not glad to see me when I go to get it."

One morning when Ted drove to the barn, a horse was standing at the

barnyard gate. It was Dark Star. Ted was glad to see him. He was glad to see Ted, too.

Ted was brushing Dark Star when the horse's new master came up to the gate. "Dark Star is a smart horse," said the man. "He lifted up a bar that locked the gate and ran from us. Do you want Dark Star back? He runs too fast for me when I ride him. I do not want to get hurt."

"Yes, sir! I want him back," said Ted. "You take the car and I will keep Dark Star. Dark Star is worth more to me than all the cars in the world."

Dark Star went into his old stall, and the man started home in his car.

"I was glad to get you back," Ted said to Dark Star. "I will never trade you for a car again."

—y

happy chilly funny pity rainy fifty
every lovely windy rocky study Polly
candy cherry merry kitty penny
sorry sunny puppy carry empty
dusty twenty copy folly foggy Betty
Henry lively softly bitterly
any many only

by my cry dry fly fry pry sly spy
try why shy sky buy

ay

day may play bay say hay lay pay
ray way clay delay tray gray spray
slay stay away jay

ey

key valley turkey they obey

By the Sea

I say
Someday
That we shall play
By the sea,
By the sand,
By the shore,

Dig wells
With shells
To fill our pails,
By the sea,
By the sand,
By the shore.

—Adele H. Seronde

The Cat

I sit soft
　On a sofa fat
And lick my velvet fur.
　I curl myself
　Into a ball
　　And purr.

—Adele H. Seronde

The Three Billy Goats

There once was a lad who had three billy goats.

All day the billy goats leaped and skipped up on a rocky hill. When it became dark and chilly, the lad drove them down to the valley.

One day, he went to meet them on the hill. But the frisky billy goats leaped over a rail into a turnip patch!

"I cannot get my goats," said the little lad. He sat on the rocky hillside and began to cry.

As he sat there, a fluffy white rabbit came along. "Why do you cry?" asked the fluffy rabbit.

"I must drive my billy goats back home," said the lad. "But they will not come from the turnip patch. That is why I am crying."

"I'll lead them away," said the fluffy rabbit. So the rabbit tried, but he had to give up. The billy goats stayed in the turnip patch. Then the fluffy rabbit sat on the rocky hillside and began to cry.

Along came a lively red fox. "Why do you cry?" asked the fox.

"This lad is crying. That is why I am crying," said the rabbit. "And the lad cannot get his billy goats.

They will not come away from the turnip patch. That is why he is crying."

"I can do it," said the fox. The fox did try to lead the billy goats away from the turnip patch. At last, he had to give up.

So the fox sat on the rocky hillside beside the lad and the rabbit. And the fox began to cry.

Then a big gray mule came along. "Why do you cry?" asked the gray mule.

"The lad's billy goats will not come away from the turnip patch," said the fox. "That is why I am crying. That is why the bunny rabbit is crying. And that is why the lad is crying."

"I'll do it!" boasted the mule. The mule did try and try and try. But he failed. The billy goats did not leave the turnip patch.

So the mule sat on the rocky hillside and began to cry.

After a while, a tiny bee buzzed over the hill. He saw all of them sitting there crying bitterly.

"Why do you cry?" said the bee softly to the mule.

"We cannot make the billy goats leave the turnip patch," said the mule. "That is why I cry. That is why the fox and the rabbit cry. And that is why the lad is crying."

"I will do it!" said the bee.

Then the big animals and the lad all stopped crying. "Ha, ha, ha. Can a tiny bee do it when we did not? What a funny little thing!"

But the tiny bee buzzed away into the turnip patch. He lit upon one of the billy goats and said, "Buzz-z-z!"

And away ran the billy goats, every one!

Silvery Flash

Silvery flash—
Silvery splash—
  a leap—
  rushes
    a fish!

Silvery hush—
Silvery gush
  of song
  at dusk—
    a thrush!

—Adele H. Seronde

Sleep, sleep,
God has His sheep
In the land of the distant sky;
Star on star,
His sheep all are
Asleep
When the far winds cry!

—Adele H. Seronde

ce

cell cent since fence brace trace
space pace race face fleece slice rice
twice place cedar center cement
central certain celery cease cellar
century celebrate success

ci

city circus cigar cinch cider cinder
circle cinnamon pencil

cy

cycle bicycle Lucy spicy fleecy

Three Mice and a Circus

Lucy and Nancy Carlson were very happy. They were going to the nearby city after lunch.

A week before, the Carlson family had been together at lunch. "Mother, what shall we do for Nancy's birthday?" said Mr. Carlson.

Nancy said, "I have saved a dollar and fifty cents. I want to spend it to celebrate my birthday." She was so excited that she waved the celery that she had in her hand.

"Careful, dear," said Mother. "That celery is not a stick for leading a band."

Nancy smiled happily and stopped waving her celery.

"Tell us where we are going to go for Nancy's birthday," said Lucy.

"We will go to the circus," said Mrs. Carlson. "It is coming to the city next week. We will all go next Saturday after lunch."

Lucy jumped down from her chair and danced in a circle. "Hurray!" she cried. "I want to see a seal and an acrobat and a clown that can ride a bicycle and . . ."

"Wait," said Nancy. "After all, it's going to be my birthday. I want to

see the trained horses and the lion and a tiger and the tumblers and . . ."

Mr. Carlson broke in. "Both of you wait, please." He got a pencil from his pocket and began to make a list. "Now, let's see—clown, seal, acrobat, lion on bicycle . . ."

"No," said Mrs. Carlson, "lions don't ride bicycles. They sit up on platforms in a circle. The lion trainer stands in the circle with a chair, a pistol, and a whip."

"O-O-O-O," said Nancy, "does he aim the pistol at the lions? Does he hurt them?"

"No, Nancy, his pistol makes a big bang, but it has no bullets in it. I don't think the lions are afraid of it. They see that it is a part of the act, to make the people get excited. The people become more excited than the lions," said Mrs. Carlson.

The next Saturday, after lunch, the family went to the city.

The circus was in a big tent, in a big grassy space at one end of the city. Beside the tent was a smaller one. It was marked in big letters—

SIDE SHOWS.

They went into the side show tent first. Inside, a man said, "See the white mice at home." He waved his stick at a little cabin.

show

Three white mice were running in front of the cabin.

Lucy said, "He is pretending that these mice are people."

There was a little white fence in front of the cabin. There was a space between the fence and the cabin. It was covered with a tiny carpet. The carpet had little green strings sticking up from it. It made a nice grassy yard for the mice to play in.

Nancy asked the circus man if the mice ever had a picnic on the grass. "It's a pretty spot," he replied, "but the mice don't take proper care of it. In place of cutting and raking the grass, they eat it. And sometimes they pull up the strings and bite them off."

"Do they ever dance on the grass?" asked Nancy. "Mother sang a song to me that told of mice dancing."

The man smiled. "That's twice today that I have been asked the

same thing. But I don't think that mice dance. At least, I've never seen them!"

Lucy said, "He's stopped pretending that they are people."

But Lucy was little, and she was getting tired. "Come on, Nancy, let's go and see the main part of the circus," Lucy said.

Mr. Carlson said, "Yes, but first I want you girls to have something to eat. What do you like?"

"I will have a stick of peppermint flavored with cinnamon," said Lucy.

Mr. Carlson smiled. "Lucy, how can peppermint candy be flavored with cinnamon?"

"If it can't," said Lucy, dancing up and down, "I just want peppermint. I like peppermint candy."

"And I want a cinnamon ice cream cone," said Nancy. "May I have one?"

"On your birthday? Certainly! But do you think there will be any cinnamon ice cream?" said Mr. Carlson.

Nancy clapped her hands. "I like vanilla! But any kind will do! I'm having a wonderful time at the circus!"

And the whole Carlson family went on into the big tent.

Those Wizards

Those wizards
Of the winter winds,
The blizzards
Blare and blow!
The ice that binds,
The hail that blinds,
White hazards
Of the snow!

—Adele H. Seronde

ge

age rage cage page stage

range change strange singe hinge

fringe plunge twinge college manage

ranger danger Roger manager stranger

germ gentle general

gi

giant ginger giblet gigantic magic

gy

dingy stingy Egypt Gypsy gym

dg dge

badge edge ledge hedge wedge sledge pledge ridge bridge dodge lodge budge nudge judge judgment fudge trudge smudge

The Wild Goats

The wild goats prance
  from ledge to ledge—
The wild goats dance
  to the very edge
Of the rocky ridge
  on a cliff so steep—
But who will bridge the sky
  with a leap?

—Adele H. Seronde

Gerald and the Stranger

In the olden days, a lad named Gerald was raised on a small farm. The farm was in a tiny kingdom far away to the East.

One day while Gerald was tending the sheep, a strange man came trudging along the road. He came over the bridge nearby, and up to the hedge by Gerald's home.

The stranger had a kind face, and he was very well dressed.

"Hello," he said, "May I stay with you for three days?"

The request seemed strange, but Gerald only said, "I will ask my father." He went inside to ask and came back in a moment. Then he told the stranger, "Yes, you may stay with us for three days."

On the first day, the stranger went with Gerald to tend the sheep. Suddenly, a fox came along. He started to attack a sheep that had strayed to the edge of the flock.

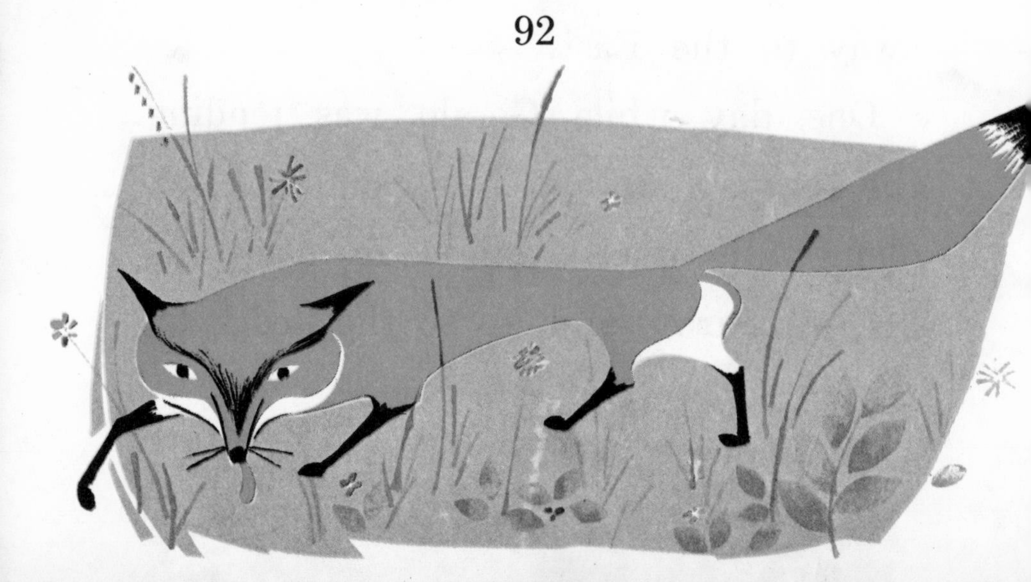

Quick as a flash, Gerald raced over and managed to drive the fox away.

The stranger was pleased with Gerald's bravery. Gerald had put himself in danger and had saved his sheep.

"You did not even have a stick," he said. "You had only your bare hands."

On the second day, it was so hot that the sun singed the grass. It made the sheep huddle together under a tree where there was a little shade.

Again the stranger went with Gerald. There was no shade and the stranger was warm. Gerald broke an armful of dry reeds and made a shelter for him.

Then the stranger said, "Gerald, you are kind as well as brave. I thank you."

On the third day, they sat in the little kitchen after a simple meal. The stranger suddenly spoke. He said, "I will give you a single wish and will promise to grant it. Will you ask for money, for fame, or for wisdom?"

Gerald said, "I will ask for wisdom, for a wise man can find riches and fame."

"Ah!" exclaimed the stranger, "I see that you are getting wise rapidly. I will not have to give you wisdom."

The stranger was a servant of the King. He had been sent to find kind and clever lads for his service. He said, "And since you are also kind and brave, you will get along well. You will be a success in the world."

Then he said, "I will start you off by making you a page to the Queen."

Gerald got along well. He became a page to the Queen of the land. Later, he was a leader of men. And at last, when he was older, he became the King's wisest adviser.

tion

station action mention position
portion addition attention nation
condition vacation education promotion
motion collection correction section

sion

expression mansion permission mission
confusion television admission

Tim Visits a Television Station

Once, at vacation time, Tim went to visit a television station. He liked to watch television programs, but he had never seen a TV station.

When he got there, a man stopped him at the gate. "Do you have permission to go inside?" the man asked Tim.

"Yes, sir," said Tim. "I have an invitation from Mr. Morgan, the station manager. Here it is."

Tim went into the station and sat down in a chair that was marked VISITORS. When it was time for the program to start, the director raised his arm. Then the action began.

Tim liked the program he saw on the stage. In the play, a rich man lived in a mansion on a hill. There

was a wicked king who wanted to take the mansion from the rich man. The king wanted to live in it himself.

But the rich man was too clever for the king. He made a lake in front of his mansion.

One morning, the king and his men started to cross the lake in boats. The rich man fired his gun at the boats and shot holes in them. The king and his men and the boats all sank to the bottom of the lake. That was the last of the wicked king.

After the program, the station manager gave Tim permission to operate one of the cameras. This was fun for Tim. "When I am big," Tim said, "I want to work in a television station."

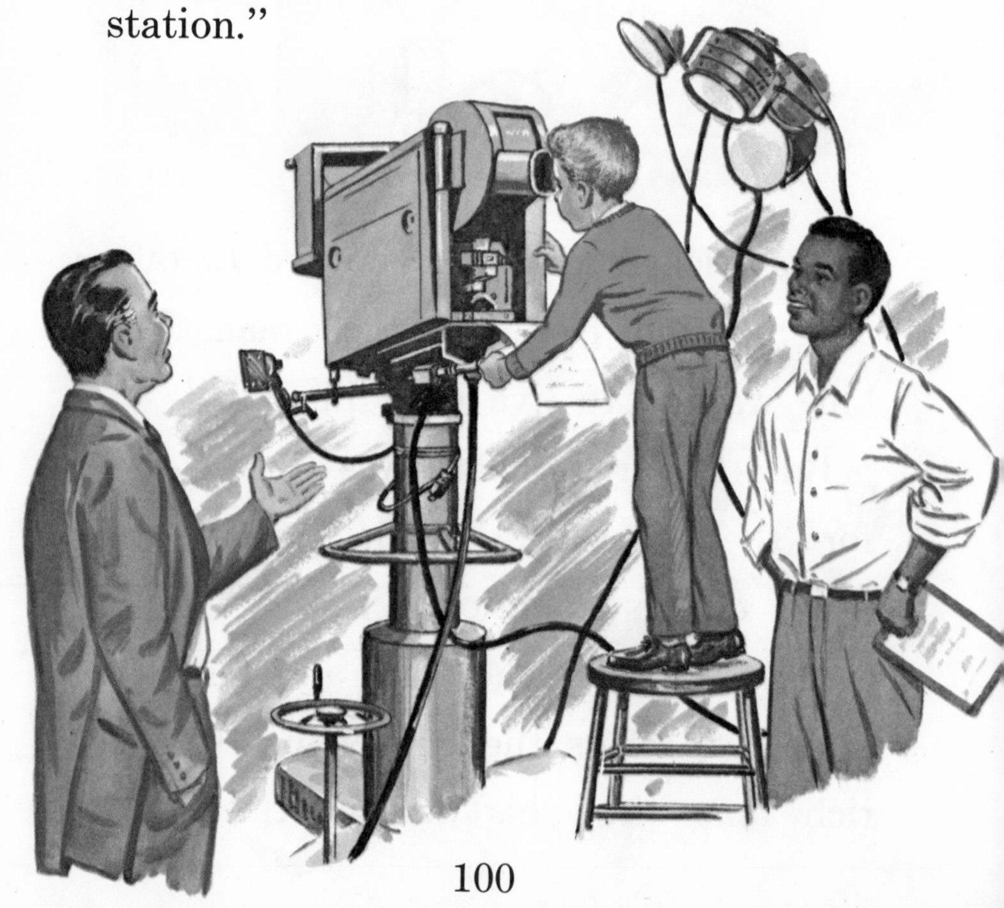

oo—as in cook

foot soot good hood book stood
wood cook hook shook took look
brook crook wool

The Rook

A rook
Sat hooked
To a crooked
Tree.
He shook
As he looked,
—Took an owl
For me!

—Adele H. Seronde

oo—as in food

food moon boot hoot loot root toot mood too proof cool pool tool stool spool room bloom boom gloom spoon soon loop droop stoop hoop goose loose broom shoot coop scoop boost groove smooth troop tooth choose coo poor

The Bat

A bat
  in an attic
Kept still,
  so still;
Still until
  the red moon
Went up
  by the hill.
"When the red moon is up,
I will not sit still!
  But I will flit
Up by the red moon
  on the hill."

—Adele H. Seronde

The Oogle-Google Goblin

Hoot Tooter was a small goblin who lived in a drain pipe. The pipe was in front of Ronny Hooper's home. It was for rain water. It ran from a pipe in the yard to the big drain under the street. It was very dark and dingy there.

Hoot was an oogle-google goblin. Hoot made a google-oogle-glup-glup, when the water ran down into the pipe. Then away it goes to the street.

Hoot, the goblin, lived in Ronny's water drain for a strange reason. The oo's in his name were the same as those in Ronny Hooper's last name. This was the first reason.

He also had a second reason for living in the pipe, as you will soon see.

One day Ronny was playing in his yard after a rainstorm. The water was gurgling down off the roof to the drain pipe. It made a last google and glug before it went to the street. Ronny was playing with a string rolled up on a spool. He made a loop at one end of the string. Then he dropped it loosely into the cool gloom inside the drain pipe.

All of a sudden, there was a big "glug," and the string jerked and shook.

Then there was a tiny cry, "O-O-O-O . . . googly-oogly-glug! Let go of my neck!"

Ronny was surprised. He paid attention to the tiny cry. He pulled up his loop of string very gently and loosely. He did not want to hurt anybody holding on to it.

Soon a tiny face and sharp ears came up from the drain. The little person, whoever he was, was holding the string. It was looped over his neck. He was holding it so that it did not pull against his throat.

"O-O-O-O!," cried Ronny. "Who are you, and are you hurt?"

"I am the oogle-google goblin. My name is Hoot Tooter, and I am not hurt. But I cannot be pulled any farther from this pipe!"

Ronny stood up and took a long look down into the pipe. He did not see very much, for it was very dingy inside. So he said, "Why not?"

The tiny person replied, "My feet are long and webby. They will not come past the turn in the drain pipe. The Queen of the Fairies put me here for a month of punishment. I am ashamed to tell you why. I was not as good as she wanted me to be. I was not as good as a good goblin is supposed to be. And I was the Queen's favorite goblin, too."

The tiny goblin looked down. He seemed to be most ashamed of himself.

"What did you do that was so bad?" asked Ronny.

"I put an ant in the Queen's buttercup," said the goblin. "And so here I am, stuck in this water drain for a month. I say oogle-google when the water runs from your drain pipe to the big drain in the street."

That was the second reason. Do you remember the first one?

Ronny said, "That is a pity." He began to like the goblin more and more. "It must be very cold and wet there in the drain. The cold rain water is running down over you so fast."

"It is," said the goblin. His expression was so sad that Ronny was sorry for him. He planned a way to set the oogle-google goblin free. He asked one more very important question—"Can you breathe very well under the water?"

"Yes, I can breathe very well down here, but I do not like it. It is cold and lonesome. It is gloomy, too."

Ronny ran indoors and went to call the gardener who took care of the yard. "Mr. Gardener," he said, "the drain in my yard is stopped up.

It makes a googly-glug when the water runs into it after a big rain. Sometimes I am afraid that it will get too full of water. It may flood the front yard. Will you please look at it the next time you come here to work?"

"Yes, Ronny, I will do that for you," said the gardener. And the very next day he came to work in Ronny's yard. He looked at the drain pipe for a while. Then he dug some dirt away from it and pulled at the pipe to fix it.

Ronny watched. He began to worry. Perhaps the goblin was being hurt. There was no cry, and soon the gardener finished his work with the drain. There was no trace of the goblin any more.

But when Ronny was in bed, a happy green goblin landed on the cover beside him. It whispered in his ear. "Thank you for getting me free and away from that terrible drain pipe. When the gardener fixed the drain, I was able to get away. The Queen of the Fairies said that I was to stay free. You were so kind to

help me escape. I had to promise to be good and never to put another ant in her buttercup."

"Now I am going to be good all the time and become her favorite goblin again. I shall always be good to you and help you if you need me."

Ronny was pleased to have a real goblin willing to help him. But he wished that the tiny goblin was still in the water pipe in his yard.

ow—as in snow

bow low blow flow row grow glow
crow mow show snow throw bowl
own sown blown grown flown owe
thrown growth yellow window elbow
hollow widow shadow slow

In the Snow

Below
In the snow
The hungry birds go
To feed
On seeds
In the winter weeds.

—Adele H. Seronde

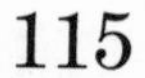

Yellow Lemon

Lemon, yellow lemon,
As yellow as the sun,
As yellow as a melon,
As a melon in the sun,
As a yellow melon mellow
In the lemon yellow sun.

—Adele H. Seronde

Little wind, blow on the hill-top,
Little wind, blow down the plain;
Little wind, blow up the sunshine,
Little wind, blow off the rain.

–Kate Greenaway

ow—as in cow

owl howl fowl scowl growl brow cow how now plow down town gown clown frown crown brown drown crowd drowsy

Down, Down!

Down, down!
Yellow and brown
The leaves are falling over the town.

ou stands for a number of sounds

house mouse pound sound found
round abound loud pouch cloud proud
bound mound ground count mount
our sour scour flour blouse out pout
spout stout trout shout south mouth

four pour court course mourn soul

soup group tour tourist your

young touch trouble southern double
country couple

Little Mouse

Little mouse,
Little mouse,
Go to sleep in your house.
The owl is abed like the cow.
The moon has gone down
To take off her gown
And the sun will be up soon now.

—Adele H. Seronde

A Little Red Apple

A little fall apple
All red, ripe, and round
Rolled into a puddle
When it fell to the ground.
The apple was able
To bobble and bound
And spin in the puddle
Around and around!

—Adele H. Seronde

The Hungry Lion

Once upon a time there was a big lion who lived in a cage at the zoo. One day, he was very hungry. When the Keeper gave him his dinner, he ate it up with one gulp of his big mouth. Quite by mistake he ate up the Keeper, too.

For a time, the Keeper was not missed. The four other Keepers sat down to lunch. As they poured some soup, they looked around the table and said, "Where is Bill?"

They looked in the Snake House—and Bill was not there.

They looked in the Parrot House—and Bill was not there.

They looked in the Tiger House—and Bill was not there.

They looked in the Big Bird House—and Bill was not there.

"Well, we cannot wait for Bill all afternoon," said the Top Animal Keeper. "The soup will get cold in our bowls."

So they sat down to eat, still wondering why young Bill was not there.

Suddenly, as they were finishing the soup, there came a loud sound of growling. The groaning came from the Lion House.

They went to see what was the matter, and there they found the big lion. They stood in a group and looked at him. He was lying on the ground looking very big and fat and not at all happy.

The Keepers looked at one another and all of them said at once, "Of course! The big lion has swallowed poor Bill!"

"We cannot leave him there," said the Top Animal Keeper, thinking carefully. "There is only one thing to do."

So they got a bottle of brown medicine from the drugstore. Then they put the big lion to sleep for the operation. With a large pair of shears they went snip, snip, snip. They cut up the front of his fur coat.

Out jumped Bill looking not a penny the worse.

They stitched the big lion up again, very carefully. When he woke up, he felt very well again.

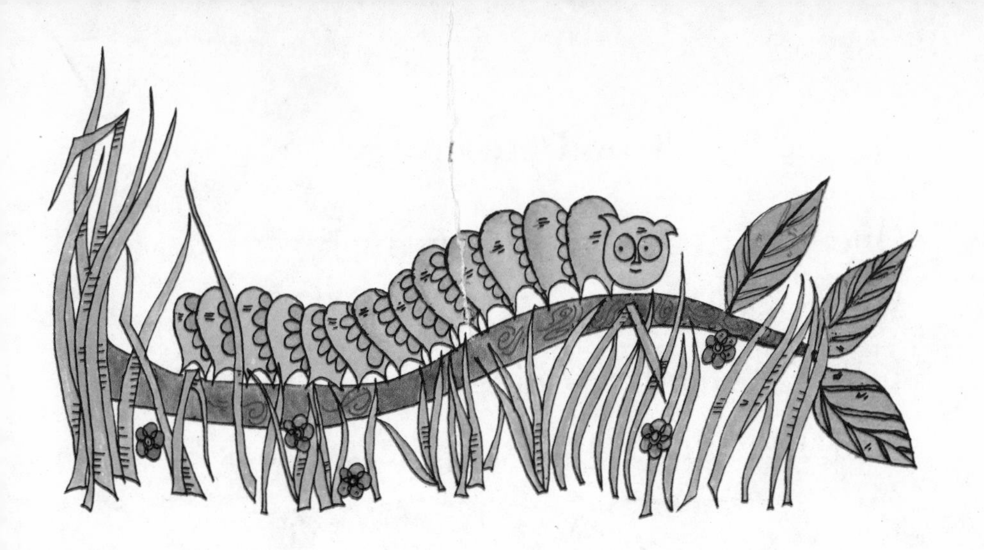

Fuzzy wuzzy, creepy crawly
  Caterpillar funny,
You will be a butterfly
  When the days are sunny.

Winging, flinging, dancing, springing
  Butterfly so yellow,
You were once a caterpillar,
  Wriggly, wiggly fellow.

—Lillian Schulz Vanada

Good Morning

One day I saw a downy duck,
With feathers on his back;
I said, "Good morning, downy duck,"
And he said, "Quack, quack, quack."

One day I saw a timid mouse,
He was so shy and meek;
I said, "Good morning, timid mouse,"
And he said, "Squeak, squeak, squeak."

One day I saw a curly dog,
I met him with a bow;
I said, "Good morning, curly dog,"
And he said, "Bow-wow-wow."

One day I saw a scarlet bird,
He woke me from my sleep;
I said, "Good morning, scarlet bird,"
And he said, "Cheep, cheep, cheep."

—Muriel Sipe

oi

join oil toil soil spoil loin noise moist boil coin joint poise point noisy voice foil hoist broil choice

oy

boy Roy oyster enjoy toy boyhood joy royal Joyce

The Shepherd Boy

There once was a shepherd boy who tended his sheep at the foot of a big hill. It was near a dark forest.

The soil there at the foot of the hill was good and moist. It made the grass nice and green. So the sheep enjoyed grazing all day.

But the shepherd boy was lonely.

shepherd

So, one day, just for fun, the boy rushed down to the village. He called out in a loud voice, "Wolf, wolf!"

The boy made quite a noise.

All of the villagers came running to join the boy and to help protect his flock.

No one saw a wolf, but some of the villagers stayed with the boy for a long time.

The boy enjoyed this so much that the next day he tried the same thing.

Again, the villagers joined him to help. But there was no wolf and they were annoyed.

Shortly after this, a wolf really came out from the forest and started to worry the sheep.

The boy quickly ran to the village. He called out in a voice much louder than before, "Wolf, wolf!"

Over and over he called, “Wolf, wolf!” and he pointed to the forest. What a fuss the boy made!

But the shepherd boy had annoyed the villagers twice before. They did not want to be fooled again. So not one of them came out to join the boy. Not one of them came to his aid.

With no one to help protect the sheep, the wolf made a good meal of the boy's flock. The wolf went away licking his lips with loud, greedy noises.

The boy was angry and sad. When the boy went to the village, the wise man told him something to remember. "Shepherd boy, now you see how important it is to tell the truth, not just now and then, but all the time."

The Swing

Swing up
To the tree-tops,
Swing down
To the grass—
The wind sings
In your swinging,
The wind sings
As you pass.

—Adele H. Seronde

Acknowledgments

Grateful acknowledgment is made for the following stories and poems to authors and publishers for permission to adapt and use their original or copyrighted material.

"Down! Down! from *Poems for Children* by Eleanor Farjeon. Copyright 1938 by Eleanor Farjeon. Published by J. B. Lippincott Company.

"Fuzzy wuzzy, creepy crawly" from *Sung Under the Silver Umbrella,* Macmillan Company, by permission of the author, Lillian Schulz Vanada.

"Good Morning" by Muriel Sipe from *Sung Under the Silver Umbrella,* Macmillan Company. Reprinted by permission of David Ross.

"Little Wind" from *Under the Window* by Kate Greenaway, reprinted by permission of the publisher, Frederick Warne and Co.

"The Hungry Lion" from *Go to Bed Book* by Ella Monckton, adapted by permission of the publishers, Frederick Warne and Co., Ltd.

"The Oogle-Google Goblin" from "The Bath Google" in *Go to Bed Book* by Ella Monckton, adapted by permission of the publisher, Frederick Warne and Co., Ltd.

"The Three Billy Goats" from "The Three Goats" in *Through the Farmyard Gate* by Emilie Poulsson, adapted by permission of the publisher, Lothrop, Lee, and Shepard Co., Inc.

Illustrations by Anna R. Atene, Gisela Jordan, Violet and Albert D. Jousset, Carol Kitzmiller, Tim H. Lofton, Elsie Jane McCorkell, Noel G. Miles, Jr., Roland V. Shutts, Edward John Smith, Barbara B. Werner, George Wilde.

Cover design by Gisela Jordan.

Sound-spelling Sequence in Grade 1

Pre-Primer

Sound	Page	Sound	Page	Sound	Page
short a	1	r	8	p	20
short e	2	s	10	dr,gr	22
short i	3	d	11	sp,mp	24
short o	4	nd	12	hard c	26
short u	5	t	14	h	28
m	6	st,nt	16	f	30
n	7	hard g	18		

Primer

Sound	Page	Sound	Page	Sound	Page
ar	1	le	22	ai	44
er	5	k	24	long i,ie	50
ed	6	ck	26	ir	51
w	7	magic e	31	long o	57
ow(cow)	12	a(care)	31	ore,or	58
l	14	long a	32	oa,oe	64
ll	15	long e,ee	36	j	68
b	21	ea	40	v	73

Reader 1-1

Sound	Page	Sound	Page	Sound	Page
sh	1	-ing	33–38	dg,dge	89
ch,tch	5	-ed	44–47	-tion,-sion	97
th	8	er as er	52	oo(cook)	101
wh	14	ar as er	53	oo(food)	102
qu	17	ir,or,ur as er	54	ow(snow)	115
x	18	-y,-ay	64	ow(cow)	118
y	19	-ey	64	ou	119
z	20	soft c	75	oi,oy	130
ng	26	soft g	88		

Reader 1-2

Sound	Page	Sound	Page	Sound	Page
long u	1	wr,kn	26	ea as long a	62
long ue	1	silent b	36	ear	62
long ui	1	silent l	36	ie as long e	72
ew,eau	8	silent g	48	ei as long e	72
aw,au	14	silent h	48	ei as long a	78
ph as f	18	silent gh	48	eigh as long a	78
hard ch	18	gh as f	48	ey as long a	78
ch as sh	18	ea as short e	62	ough	101

Basic Sounds of the English Language

UNVOICED CONSONANTS

f	fat
h	hat
k (c)	kit cat
p	pan
s	set
t	ten
ch (tch)	chin match
sh	ship
th	thin
wh	when

VOICED CONSONANTS

b	bat
d	dig
g	get
j (dg)	jet edge
l	lad
m	man
n	net
ng	sing
r	ran
th	then
v	van
w	wet
y	yes
z	zoo
zh	measure

PURE VOWELS

a	bat
a	father barn
a	ball saw water
a	chair dare wear
e	bet
e	Pete theme
i	sit
o	got
u	cut
u	put book
u	boot
a	above
er	cedar her third word burn

DIPHTHONGS

a	hate
ou - ow	out cow
oi - oy	soil boy
i	time
o	go
u	use mute few